Handwriting

In Year One (age 5+) your child is expected to be able to:

- Sit correctly at a table and hold their pencil correctly and comfortably.

- Begin to form lower-case letters in the correct direction, starting and finishing in the right place.

- Form capital letters and digits 0 – 9.

- Understand which letters belong to which handwriting 'families' (letters that are formed in similar ways) and practise writing these.

Designed by Plum5
Illustrations by Sue King, Sharon Smart and Andy Geeson
Educational consultant Chris Andrew and Nina Filipek

Autumn
Publishing

Shapes

Start at the dot and trace over the dashes to draw these shapes. Try to keep your pencil on the paper for the whole time.

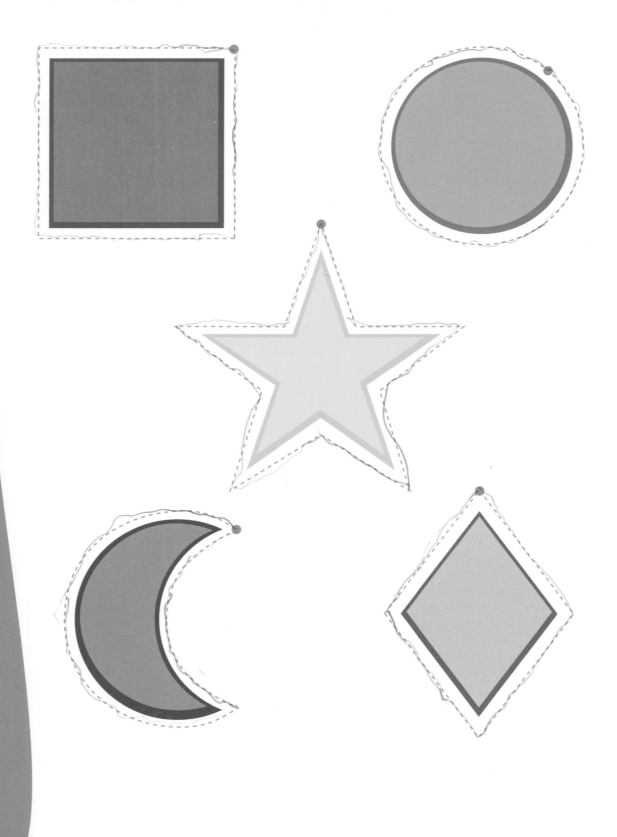

Writing patterns

Start at the dots and trace over the dashes.

Start at the dot. Look at the direction of the arrows and trace over the dashes. Then write the patterns yourself.

MMM

UUU

CCoo

Letter patterns

Straight lines and curves
Look at the direction of the arrows
and trace over the dashes.
Then write the letters yourself.

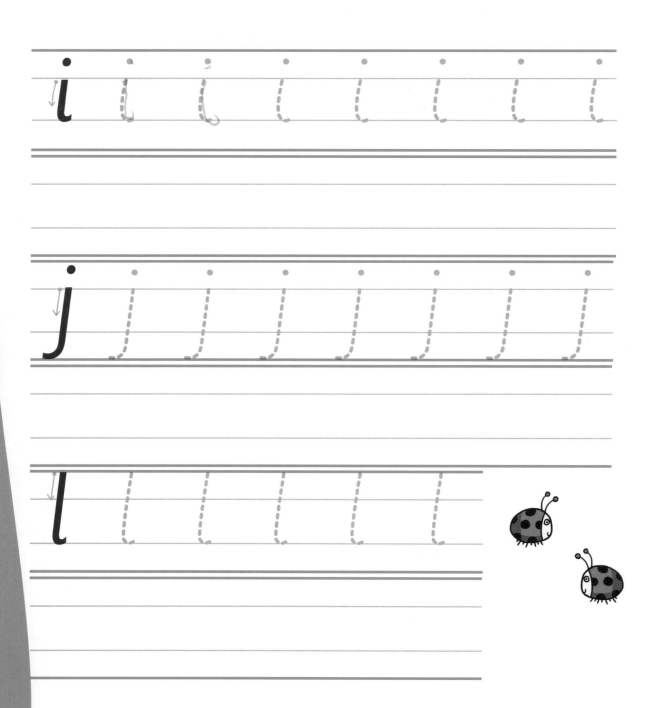

y y y y y y y y y

u u u u u u u u

t t t t t t t t

More letter patterns

Up and down strokes

Look at the direction of the arrows and trace over the dashes.
Then write the letters yourself.

n n n n n n n n n

m m m m m m m

r r r r r r r r

h h h h h h h h h

b b b b b b b b b

p p p p p p p p

More letter patterns

Half circle and circle

Look at the direction of the arrows and trace over the dashes.
Then write the letters yourself.

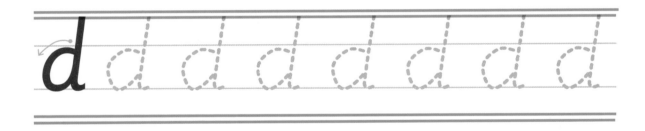

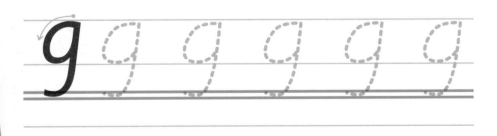

c c c c c c c c

q q q q q q q q

e e e e e e e e

o o o o o o o o

Complex letters

Look at the direction of the arrows and trace over the dashes.
Then write the letters yourself.

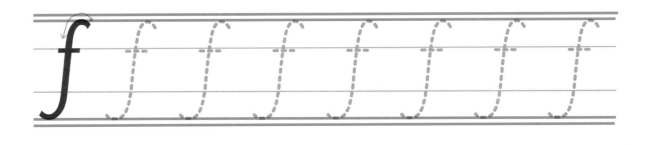

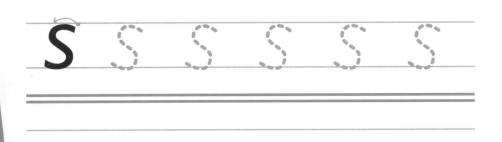

z z z z z z z z z z z z z z

v v v v v v v v v v v v v v

x x x x x x x x x x x x x x

k k k k k k k k k k k k

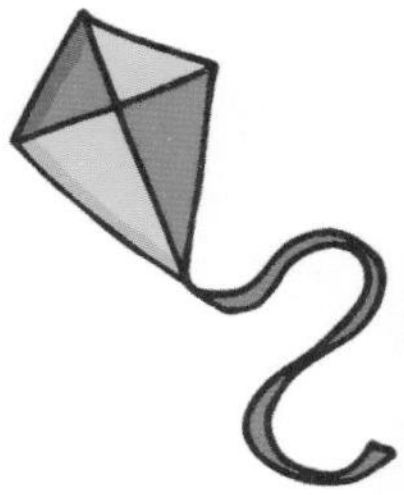

Letter formation

Trace and copy the letters of the alphabet.

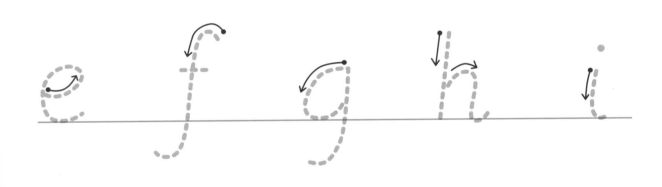

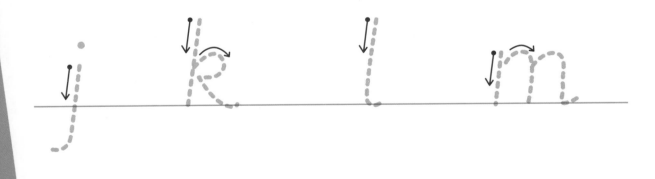

n o p q

r s t u v

w x y z

Joining strokes

To do joined-up writing you add **exit** strokes at the base of some letters. Trace over the dashes, then write the letters yourself.

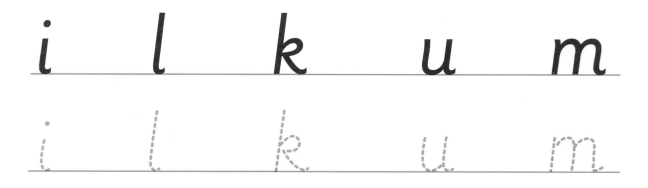

i l k u m

i l k u m

n a d e t c

n a d e t c

More joining strokes

Letters based on a half-circle or circle can have joining strokes at the **beginning**. Trace over the dashes, then write the letters yourself.

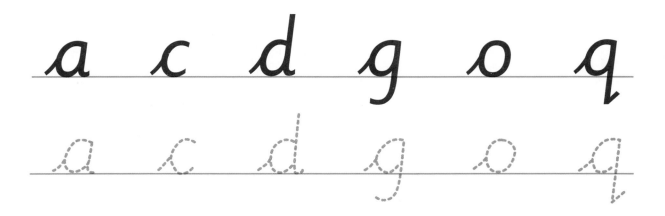

a   c   d   g   o   q

a   c   d   g   o   q

Practise:

ad   do   oc   ag

ad   do   oc   ag

More joining strokes

Some letters have exit strokes at the **top** of the letter.
Trace over the dashes, then write the letters yourself.

σ   r   v   w

σ   r   v   w

Practise:

σσ   rrr   vv   ww

σσ   rr   vv   ww

More joining strokes

The letters **f** and **t** sometimes have different kinds of joining strokes. Trace over the dashes, then write the letters yourself.

f or f	f f		
t or t	t t		

fl   ef   tu   tr

fl   ef   tu   tr

Some letters can be joined with a loop, or they can be left unjoined.

g or g   j or j   y or y

g g   j j   y y

More joining strokes

This is how to join the remaining letters of the alphabet.
These letters can be joined or left unjoined.
Trace over the dashes, then write the letters yourself.

p   b   z   x   s

ph   br   bl

ph   br   bl

ox   box   zoo

ox   box   zoo

Pairs of joined-up letters

Here are some examples of pairs of joined-up letters.
Trace over the dashes, then write the words on the lines.

poppy

kitten

lorry

moon

teddy

geese

Practise joined-up writing

Copy the words on the lines under each picture.
Try to keep your pencil on the paper for each word.

a puppy and a poppy

a kitten and a mitten

a moon and a balloon

a frog sits on a log

Capital letters

Copy the letters of the alphabet as capital letters.

N O P Q

R S T U V

W X Y Z

Practise capital letters

Write the capital letters for the days of the week, and the months on the opposite page.

_unday

_onday

_uesday

_ednesday

_hursday

_riday

_aturday

_pril

_uly

_ctober

_ecember

Write the sentences on the lines.

Children play in the leaves.

_____

Leaves fall from trees.

_____

We love playing in the waves.

Ice cream is lovely.

Write the sentences on the lines.

Birthday cakes need candles.

_____

Then we blow them out.

_____

Phonics

In Year One (age 5+) your child is expected to be able to:

- Apply phonic knowledge and skills to decode words.

- Respond quickly with the correct sound to graphemes (letters or groups of letters) for all 40+ phonemes, including alternative sounds for graphemes.

- Read accurately by blending sounds in unfamiliar words containing GPCs that have been taught.

Glossary

Graphemes: a letter or group of letters representing one sound, e.g. sh, ch, igh, ough (as in 'though').

Phonemes: the smallest single identifiable sound, e.g. sh represents just one sound, but 'sp' represents two.

GPC: This stands for grapheme-phoneme correspondence and is the relationship between sounds and the letters which represent those sounds. This is also referred to as 'letter-sound correspondences'.

First letter sounds

Look at the pictures. The first letters (graphemes) are missing.
Say the word, sound it out and write in the missing letter.

__nt

__an

__og

__ish

__et

__at

__oot

__at

__gg

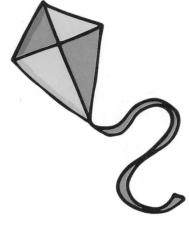

__ite

__un

__enguin

Look at the pictures. The first letters (graphemes) are missing.
Say the word, sound it out and write in the missing letter.

__anana

__an

__up

__ose

__one

__ctopus

Initial sounds

Look at the pictures. The first sounds are missing. These sounds are made up of two graphemes. Say the word, sound it out and write in the missing letters. You can choose from **ch**, **sh**, **qu** or **th**.

ch sh qu th

___ick

___ip

___een

___ink

___air

___ark

End letter sounds

Look at the pictures. The last letters (graphemes) are missing. Say the word, sound it out and write in the missing letter.

ja__

fro__

mo__

ca__

hamste__

bir__

fla__

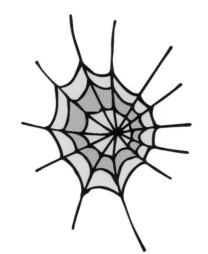

fo__

we__

su__

he__

cra__

More end letter sounds

Look at the pictures. The last letters (graphemes) are missing.
Say the word, sound it out and write in the missing letter.
You can choose from **nk** or **ng** or **ck**.

nk

ng

ck

ki___

dri___

ri___

cli___

thi___

First and last sounds

Look at the pictures. The first and last letters (graphemes) are missing.
Say the word, sound it out and write in the missing letters.

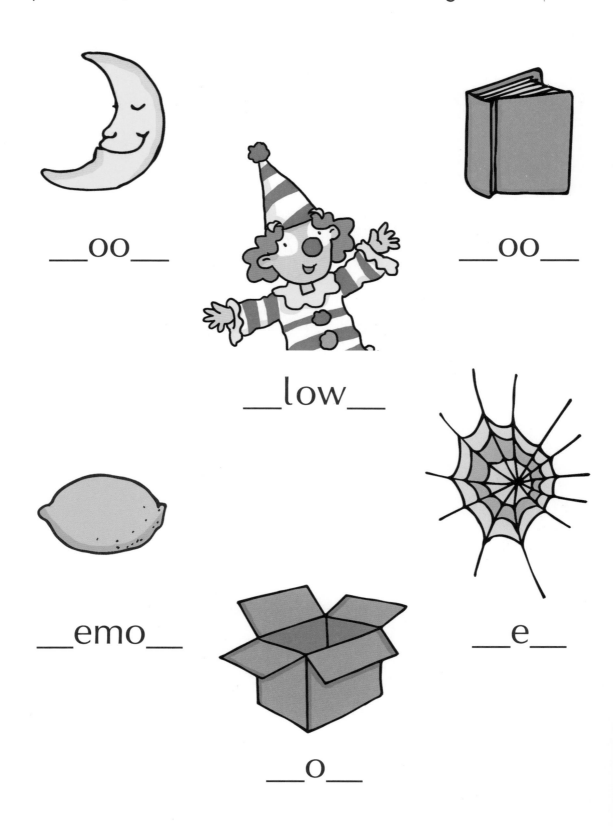

__oo__

__oo__

__low__

__emo__

__e__

__o__

Rhyming words

Rhyming words sound the same at the end of the words, like box and fox. Look at the pictures and the words underneath. Match the rhyming words together by drawing a line between them.

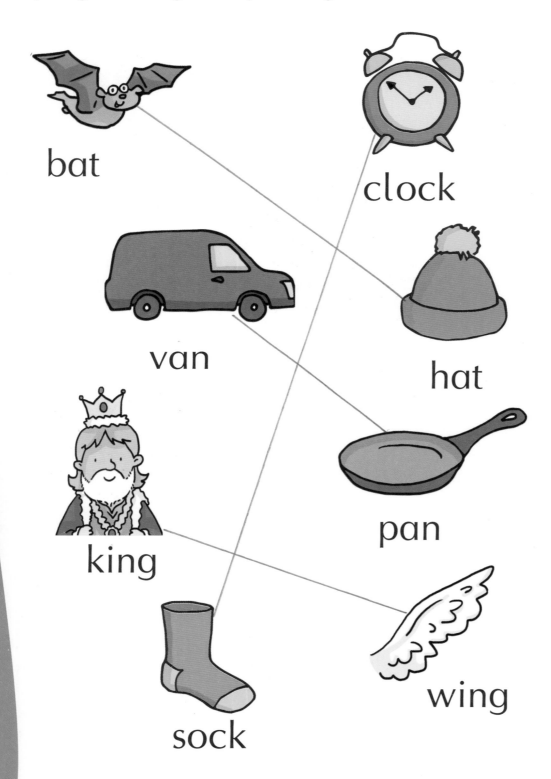

bat

clock

van

hat

king

pan

sock

wing

mug

pen

ten

boy

frog

rug

toy

dog

Middle letter sounds

Look at the pictures, say the word, sound it out and work out what the missing sound is. Write the letter in the space.

h_a_t

m_a_p

p_i_n

m_o_p

c_o_t

b_a_t

Brilliant blending

When two letters are put together to make one sound they are called a digraph. Fill in the blanks with the correct consonant blends. Choose from the tiles below.

fr   br   cr   cl   pl   fl   gl   gr   dr

b_ead

___og

___y

___ant

___oud

___ock

___ue

___ab

___ush

More brilliant blending

Fill in the blanks with the correct consonant blends.
Choose from the tiles below.

st

sn

cr

cl

gr

fl

dr

ch

_ch_ air

___ick

___ink

___air

___own

___owman

___ower

___um

___apes

Amazing ending blending

Fill in the blanks at the end of the word with the correct consonant blends. Choose from the tiles below.

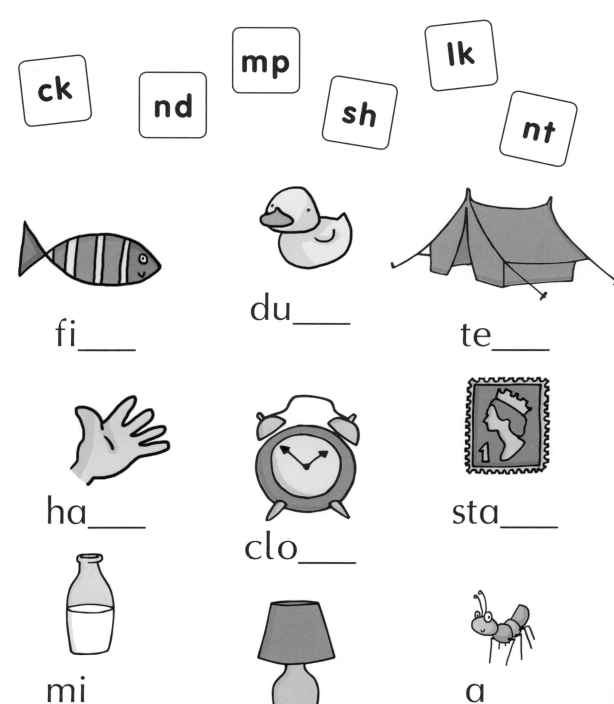

ck

nd

mp

sh

lk

nt

fi___

du___

te___

ha___

clo___

sta___

mi___

la___

a___

Playing in the rain

Look at the words below. You can choose either **ay** or **ai** to go in the missing spaces:

st___

r___n

w___

tr___n

d___

p___nt

pl___

w___t

tr___

Get a fright

What three letters make the sound i? **igh** makes a sound like a long i. Make these words make sense by adding **igh**.

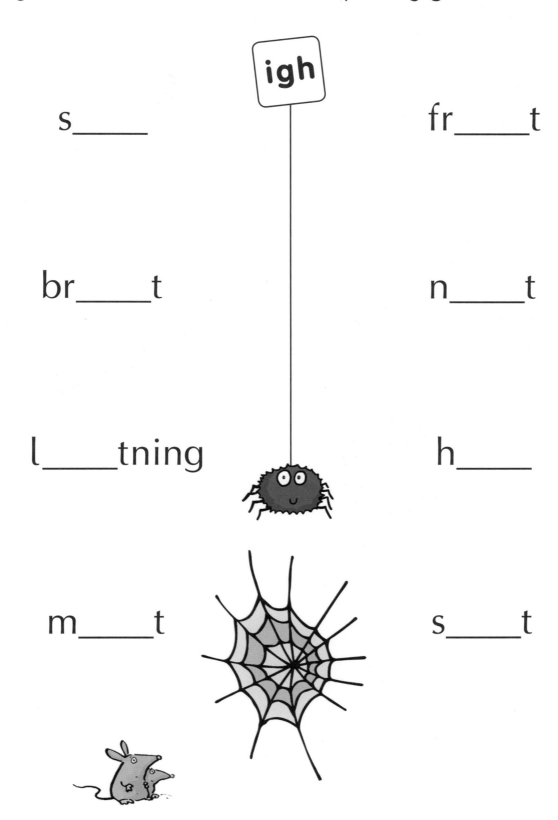

s____

fr____t

br____t

n____t

l____tning

h____

m____t

s____t

Ar or or?

Draw lines from the pictures to the correct sound (digraph).
Write the words in the correct box.

or

ar

Air or ir?

Write the correct sounds into the words below.

air   ir

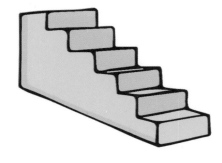

st____

b____d

f____

ecl____

ch____

g____l

Sound out

Circle the pictures that make the sound **ou** like in house.

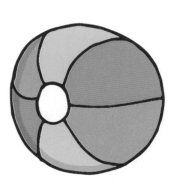

Ou or ow?

Draw lines from the pictures to the correct sound (digraph).
Write the words in the correct box.

OU

OW

Draw lines from the pictures to the correct sound (digraph).

oi

oy

Ow or oa?

Look at the pictures below. Find the words from the word bank that match these pictures, and write them in the correct boxes.

a.

b.

c.

d.

e.

f.

arrow

window

goat

coach

snow

coat

Are you sure?

Read the words out loud, choose one from each group and draw a picture of it in the frame.

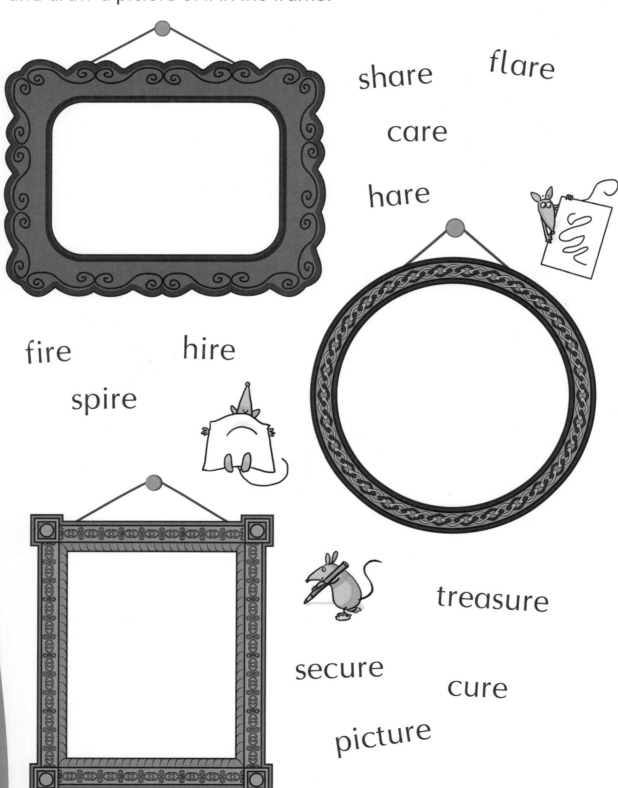

share   flare

care

hare

fire   hire

spire

treasure

secure   cure

picture

Atten-shun!

Words ending with **tion** as in nation sound like (shun).
Words ending with **sion** as in vision also sound like (shun).
Find words ending in these sounds in the word search below.

r	i	s	e	c	t	i	o	n	k
e	x	v	r	i	g	e	q	d	v
a	i	y	j	a	i	m	i	z	s
c	o	n	f	e	s	s	i	o	n
t	i	l	l	u	s	i	o	n	x
i	a	d	d	i	t	i	o	n	h
o	d	e	c	i	s	i	o	n	f
n	s	t	a	t	i	o	n	k	c
o	u	s	e	s	s	i	o	n	v
t	n	f	b	y	c	x	p	k	d

section   confession   reaction

station   illusion   decision

addition   session

Happy endings

Colour in the correct spelling to end each sentence, and then write it in the space provided.

Listen! I need your full _____

attenshun	attencian
attention	attenshon

If you don't understand,
you ask for an _____

explanasion	explanacian
explanashun	explanation

Another way of
saying adding is _____

addician	addition
addision	addishun

Fireworks are like an _____

exploshun

explotion

explosion

explocian

If you bump in
to someone this
can be called a _____

collision

collishun

collition

collician

If you say that someone
can do something, you
have given them _____

permition

permician

permishun

permission

You're the teacher!

Look at the sentences below. Which are correct?
Give them a ✔ if they are correct or circle any mistakes
and write the correct word beneath.

a. England is a nation.

b. Is there anything good on television?

c. It is my ambision to be a writer.

d. When are you going to the station?

e. Illutions are my favourite type of magic.

No nonsense!

Using the consonant blends below and some vowels make up some nonsense words that might describe a fruit.
You might describe how they look, taste, smell or feel!

e.g. That apple smells **flurpy** or that pear tastes **glucky**!

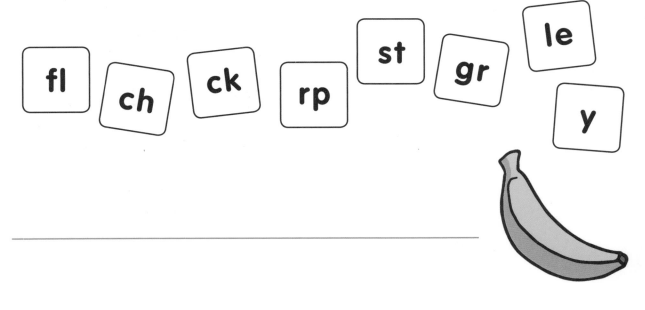

_____

_____

Nonsense words

Circle the words below which are nonsense words.
Then pick your favourite nonsense word and draw a picture
of it in the frame opposite!

robot

kear

vurk   queen

boot   kite

chick

queck   jigh

thorden

zurd   coat

duck

nud

kitten   flurp

plab

Nud

Answers

First letter sounds
<u>a</u>nt, <u>p</u>an, <u>d</u>og, <u>f</u>ish, <u>n</u>et, <u>r</u>at, <u>b</u>oot, <u>h</u>at, <u>e</u>gg, <u>k</u>ite, <u>s</u>un, <u>p</u>enguin

More first letter sounds
<u>b</u>anana, <u>f</u>an, <u>c</u>up, <u>n</u>ose, <u>b</u>one, <u>o</u>ctopus

Initial sounds
<u>ch</u>ick, <u>sh</u>ip, <u>qu</u>een, <u>th</u>ink, <u>ch</u>air, <u>sh</u>ark

End letter sounds
ja<u>r</u>, fro<u>g</u>, mo<u>p</u>, hamste<u>r</u>, ca<u>t</u>, bir<u>d</u>, fla<u>g</u>, we<u>b</u>, fo<u>x</u>, su<u>n</u>, he<u>n</u>, cra<u>b</u>

More end letter sounds
ki<u>ng</u>, dri<u>nk</u>, ri<u>ng</u>, cli<u>ck</u>, thi<u>nk</u>

First and last sounds
<u>m</u>oo<u>n</u>, <u>c</u>low<u>n</u>, <u>b</u>oo<u>k</u>, <u>l</u>emo<u>n</u>, <u>b</u>o<u>x</u>, <u>w</u>e<u>b</u>

Rhyming words
bat - hat, clock - sock, van - pan, king - wing, mug - rug, pen - ten, frog - dog, toy - boy

Middle letter sounds
h<u>a</u>t, m<u>a</u>p, p<u>i</u>n, m<u>o</u>p, c<u>o</u>t, b<u>a</u>t

Brilliant blending
<u>br</u>ead, <u>fr</u>og, <u>fl</u>y, <u>pl</u>ant, <u>cl</u>oud, <u>cl</u>ock, <u>gl</u>ue, <u>cr</u>ab, <u>br</u>ush

More brilliant blending
<u>ch</u>air, <u>cl</u>ick, <u>dr</u>ink, <u>st</u>air, <u>cr</u>own, <u>sn</u>owman, <u>fl</u>ower, <u>dr</u>um, <u>gr</u>apes

Amazing ending blending
fi<u>sh</u>, du<u>ck</u>, te<u>nt</u>, ha<u>nd</u>, clo<u>ck</u>, sta<u>mp</u>, mi<u>lk</u>, la<u>mp</u>, a<u>nt</u>

Playing in the rain
r<u>ai</u>n, st<u>ay</u>, w<u>ay</u>, d<u>ay</u>, tr<u>ai</u>n, p<u>ai</u>nt, w<u>ai</u>t, pl<u>ay</u>, tr<u>ay</u>

Get a fright
s<u>igh</u>, fr<u>igh</u>t, br<u>igh</u>t, n<u>igh</u>t, l<u>igh</u>tning, h<u>igh</u>, m<u>igh</u>t, s<u>igh</u>t

Ar or or?
ar st<u>ar</u>, c<u>ar</u>, j<u>ar</u>
or c<u>or</u>n, f<u>or</u>k, th<u>or</u>n

Air or ir?
air st<u>air</u>, f<u>air</u>, ecl<u>air</u>, ch<u>air</u>
ir b<u>ir</u>d, g<u>ir</u>l

Sound out
h<u>ou</u>se, m<u>ou</u>se

Ou or ow?
ou cl<u>ou</u>d, h<u>ou</u>se, m<u>ou</u>se
ow cl<u>ow</u>n, cr<u>ow</u>n, fl<u>ow</u>er

Oy or oi?
oy b<u>oy</u>, t<u>oy</u>
oi p<u>oi</u>nt, c<u>oi</u>n, f<u>oi</u>l, t<u>oi</u>let

Ow or oa?
a. sn<u>ow</u>, **b.** c<u>oa</u>ch, **c.** arr<u>ow</u>, **d.** wind<u>ow</u>, **e.** g<u>oa</u>t **f.** c<u>oa</u>t

Atten-shun!

r	i	s	e	c	t	i	o	n	k
e	x	v	r	i	g	e	q	d	v
a	i	y	j	a	i	m	i	z	s
c	o	n	f	e	s	s	i	o	n
t	i	l	l	u	s	i	o	n	x
i	a	d	d	i	t	i	o	n	h
o	d	e	c	i	s	i	o	n	f
n	s	t	a	t	i	o	n	k	c
o	u	s	e	s	s	i	o	n	v
t	n	f	b	y	c	x	p	k	d

Happy endings
Listen! I need your full **attention**.
If you don't understand, you ask for an **explanation**.
Another way of saying adding is **addition**.
Fireworks are like an **explosion**.
If you bump in to someone this can be called a **collision**.
If you say that someone can do something, you have given them **permission**.

You're the teacher!
Correct **a d**
b. television - television
c. ambision - ambition
e. Illutions - Illusions

Nonsense words
vurk, kear, queck, jigh, zurd, thorden, nud, flurp, plab

Spelling

In Year One (age 5+) your child is expected to be able to:

• Spell: words containing the 40+ phonemes taught; common exception words; the days of the week.

• Name the letters of the alphabet in order, and use letter names to distinguish between alternative spellings of the same sound.

• Add prefixes and suffixes including adding –s or –es; the prefix un-; and the suffixes –ing, -ed and –est where there is no change to the spelling of the root word.

• Apply simple spelling rules and guidance.

Glossary

Phonemes: the smallest single identifiable sound, e.g. sh represents just one sound, but 'sp' represents two.

CVC words (consonant vowel consonant)

All of the words below have a vowel missing.
Write in the missing letters.

c_a_t   b___d

f___n   c___w   d___g

h___n   n___t

Write in the correct vowels to complete the words.

k__ng

fl__g

b___rd

fr__g

dr__m

sh__p

h__rp

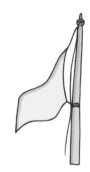

m___st

sw__m

'ch', 'sh', 'th' and 'wh' words

Look at the words in the boxes and colour any that have a **ch** sound blue, a **sh** sound red, a **th** sound green and a **wh** sound yellow.

shell	moth	chop
thin	chip	wish
when	with	fish

Now, using the sounds below, complete the words. Some sounds will go at the start of the word, some at the end. Watch out - you may be able to use more than one sound for some words!

ch   sh   th   wh

____ape   wa____   ____urch

wi____   mu____   ____ich

Using the sounds in the boxes below complete the words. There may be more than one sound that works!

she____   mo____   so____   du____

be____   bu____   fi____

Now look at the words in the boxes and colour any that have a **ss** sound blue, a **ll** sound red, a **zz** sound green, a **ck** purple and an **ff** sound yellow.

ball	fizz	shall
block	muck	moss
pass	buzz	fluff

Thinking of fishing

Look at the words in the boxes and shade any that have an **ng** sound blue and an **nk** sound red. Look out, some don't have either!

link	thing	plank
sing	sprinkle	clunk
wand	croak	along

Now look at the picture. Which line does not lead to a word that ends in **ng** or **nk?** Write your answer in the box.

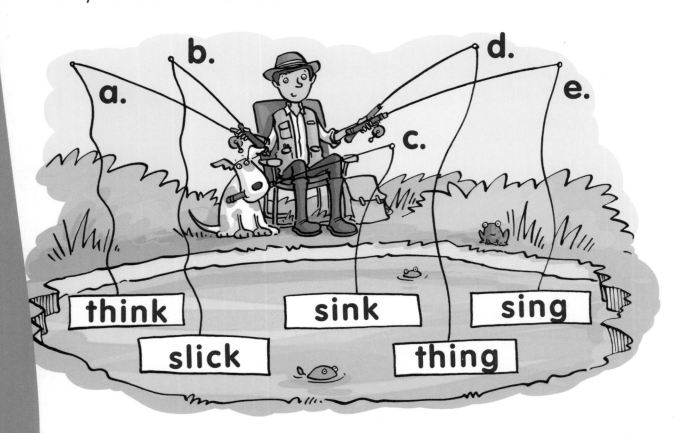

think   sink   sing

slick   thing

Words ending in 'tch' and 've'

Look at the words below. Some of them have the **tch** sound and the others have the **ve** sound. Draw a line from each word to the correct sound.

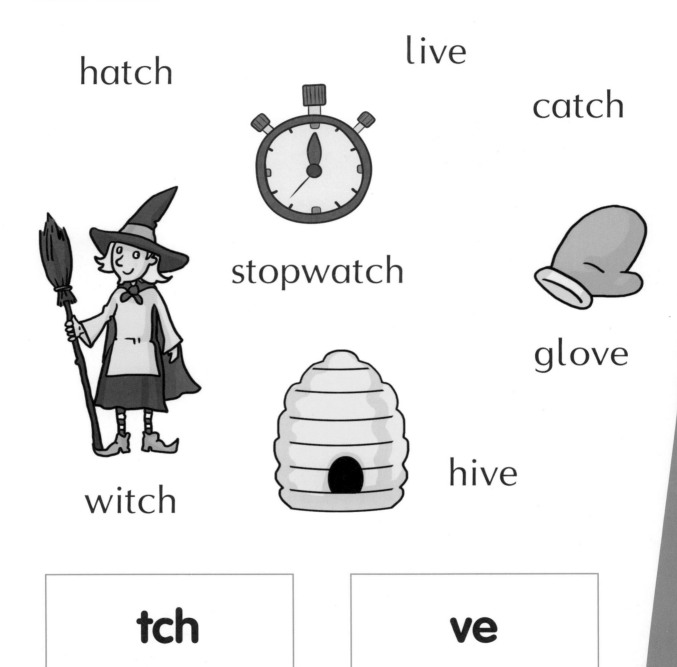

live

hatch

catch

stopwatch

glove

hive

witch

tch	ve

Words ending in 's' and 'es'

The words below are **plurals**. That means there is more than one of each thing. Colour in the words that end in **es** blue and say them out loud. What do you notice about them?
They have an extra beat to the word – try clapping it out.
e.g. dog**s** = 1 clap   match**es** = 2 claps

witches

catches

cats

thanks

bags

foxes

matches

spends

boxes

rocks

balls

hatches

dogs

lamps

Comparisons

We add on the endings **er** or **est** to compare things.
For example: short – short**er** – short**est**.
Look at the words below. Can you add **er** or **est** on to these words?

	er	**est**
fast	fast_____	fast_____
tall	tall_____	tall_____
low	low_____	low_____
kind	_____	_____
grand	_____	_____

Can you think of some of your own?

_____ _____ _____

_____ _____ _____

Look at the words in the boxes and choose one for each of the endings below. Which words can be used with both **er** and **est**? Colour them in red.

slow

quick

hunt

buzz

show

low

play

old

strong

hard

flow

spray

_____er   _____est

_____er   _____est

_____er   _____est

_____er   _____est

_____er   _____est

_____er   _____est

Words ending in 'ay' and 'oy'

Can you think of some words that end in **ay**? Write them below.

___m__ay   ___ay   ___ay   ___ay

Now think of some words that end in **oy**. Write them below.

___oy   ___oy   ___oy   ___oy

See how many **ay** and **oy** words you can find in this word search.
Five is good, eight is excellent, over 10 is magnificent!

c	l	s	p	x	v	g	t	f
s	a	t	y	p	m	e	f	t
t	y	r	a	v	a	t	x	o
a	l	a	w	k	y	r	m	y
y	z	y	z	w	f	a	a	g
s	t	b	y	h	k	y	f	s
u	y	c	o	y	s	b	h	j
h	z	a	b	j	o	y	n	e
t	e	b	d	h	w	t	n	v

You're the teacher!

Some words have an **ay** sound in them that looks like **ai**.
Look at the words below and circle the spellings that are correct.

rain   wayt   trayn
rayn   wait   train

afraid   fayl   tail
afrayd   fail   tayl

Some words have an **oy** sound in them that looks like **oi**.
Look at the words below and circle the spellings that are incorrect.

oyl   spoil   joyn
oil   spoyl   join

point   soil   boyl
poynt   soyl   boil

Make a cake!

Some words have an **ay** sound but are actually written like this:

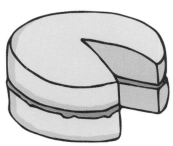

c<u>a</u>k<u>e</u>

consonant + **a** + consonant + **e**

You could call this letter sequence 'make a cake' to help you remember the spelling.

Try it with these words then match them to the pictures. Write out the words then draw a line from the correct word to the right picture.

cake	lake	flame	game

__a__e

__a__e

__a__e

__ __a__e

Five alive

You could call this 'five alive' because the spelling pattern is

f<u>i</u>v<u>e</u>   consonant + **i** + consonant + **e**

Find as many **i_e** words as you can in the word search.

five	time	~~nine~~
ride	side	life
like	~~line~~	
hike	hide	

x	n	y	l	i	k	e	m	x	x
h	i	j	g	r	d	k	j	s	t
p	n	b	l	i	s	a	h	e	i
a	e	m	i	d	i	c	i	o	m
l	y	f	n	e	d	w	d	h	e
i	l	i	e	s	t	r	e	t	h
f	i	v	d	s	i	d	e	u	e
e	k	e	a	m	r	s	w	d	k
l	i	n	m	h	i	k	e	b	i
x	q	m	y	x	y	b	o	i	k

Spelling patterns

Can you spot the spelling pattern in the words below?

home

those

woke

slope

hope

hole

pole

rope

stole

bone

That's right the vowels go **o** then **e**.

Can you write a silly sentence that uses lots of these words?
e.g. **Can you imagine a rabbit hole so deep that you need a rope to get up the slope!**

_____

_____

_____

More spelling patterns

Can you spot the spelling patterns in the words below?

June	rule	rude	cute
tube	tune	cube	
fume	glue		use

That's right the vowels go **u** then **e**!

Do you sound out the **e** when you say the words?
No, but it does change how we pronounce the **u** –
it sounds more like **oo**.
Make up a silly sentence for this set of words.

_____

_____

_____

Words with 'ar' and 'ee'

Choose which letters complete each word – **ar** or **ee**?

st____   g____den   sh____p

asl____p   c____   h____p

p____k   b____

Words with 'ea'

Some words are spelled with **ea**, but sound like **ee**.
Which ones are correct? Put a circle around them.

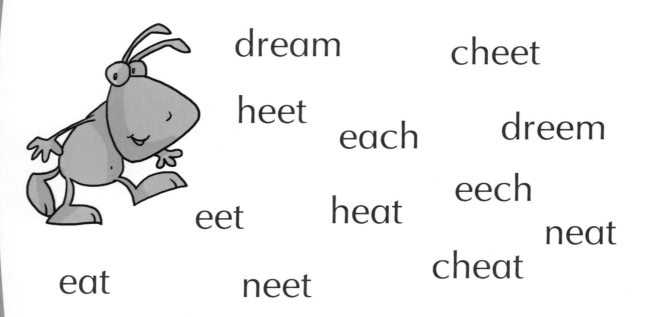

dream   cheet

heet
          each   dreem

                          eech

eet   heat
                          neat

                    cheat

eat   neet

Other words are spelled with **ea**, but sound like **e**.
Which ones are correct? Put a ring around them.

head   heavy

          stedy
                                    insted

steady
                    hed

instead   hevy

                    def

deaf

Words with 'er'

Complete the crossword below. Here's a clue - it only contains **er** words!

1. Not sweet, it's bitt__

2. Season after spring

3. Not over but und__

4.→ The coldest season

4.↓ When it's not so cold

5. Opposite of brother

Scramble mania!

Some words have the same sound when we say them but are spelt differently. Words with **ir** and **ur** are like this. Unscramble the words below.

irbd <u>b i r d</u>

trihs <u>s h i r t</u>

lirg <u>g i r l</u>

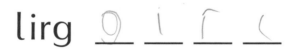

ridht <u>t h i r d</u>

nurse

surne _ _ _ _ _ _

arihc _ _ _ _ _ _

rulcs _ _ _ _ _ _

urnb _ _ _ _ _

aarlipen _ _ _ _ _ _ _ _

On the right road

All of the words below have **oa** in the middle. Complete the words and then draw a line to the matching picture.

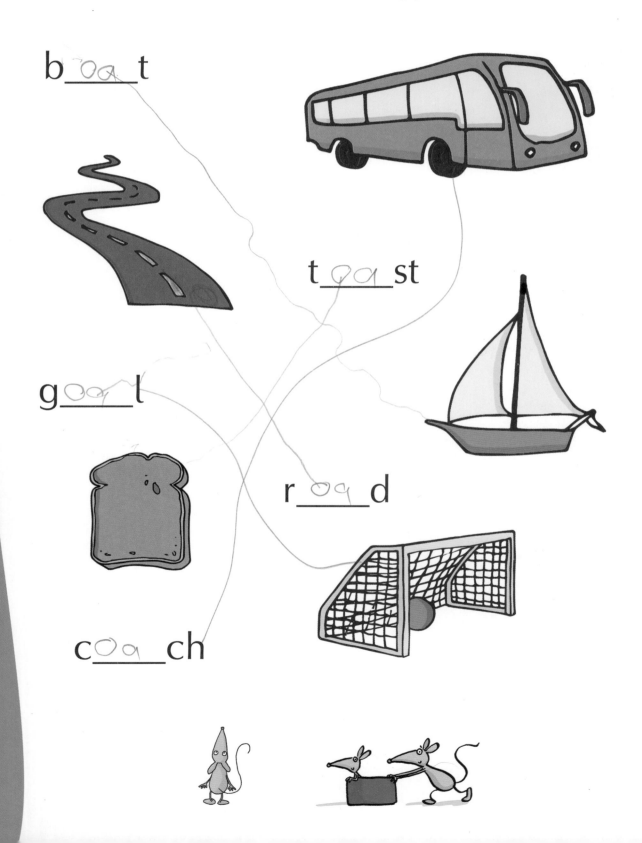

b_oa_t

t_oa_st

g_oa_l

r_oa_d

c_oa_ch

Words with 'ew' and 'ue' sound the same but are spelt differently. Look at the words below and write them in the correct box.

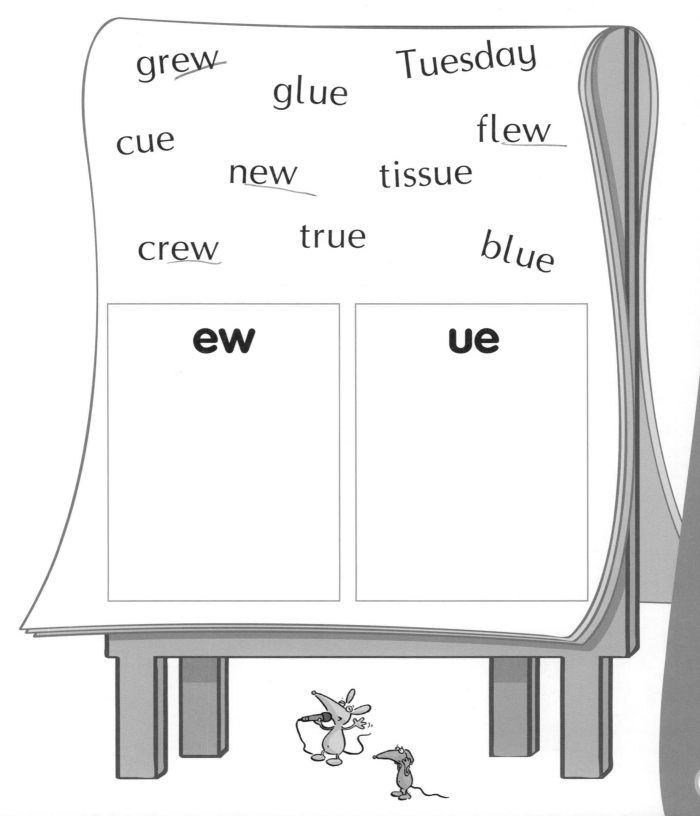

grew

glue

Tuesday

cue

flew

new

tissue

crew

true

blue

ew	ue

Words with 'ou' and 'ow'

Fill in the missing letters of these **ow** words.

c____   sn____   b_ow_

fl____er   t____n   cr____n

Now see if you can unscramble these words: they are all **ou** words.

oushe _____

ousnd _____

mseou _____

Words ending in 'y'

All of these words end in **y**.
Using the picture clues, write the missing letters.

_ _ _ _ _ y

_ _ _ y

_ _ _ _ _ _ y

_ _ _ _ y

_ _ _ _ y

_ _ y

Whales and dolphins

ph can sound a bit like **f** when spelling – don't fall into this trap!
Look at these words and cross out the incorrect spellings.

dolphin   dolfin

elefant   elephant

alphabet   alfabet

phone   fone

wh can be tricky too because you don't always hear the **h**.
Write the **wh** words next to the pictures.

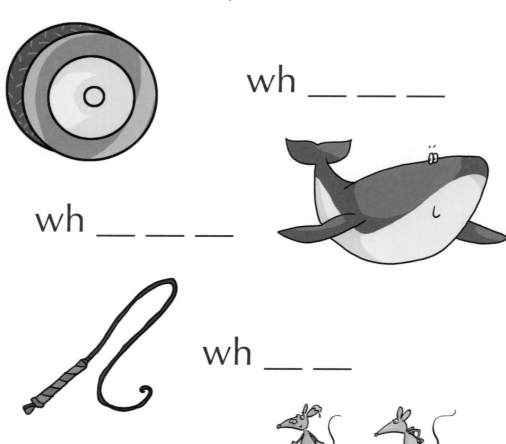

wh __ __ __

wh __ __ __

wh __ __

90

ie or igh?

ie and **igh** sound the same. One way to remember which way to spell a word with this sound is that 3 letter words end in **ie**.
e.g: **lie**, **tie**, **pie** and **die**.
Longer words tend use **igh**
e.g: **sigh**, **light**, **right** and **fright**.

Have a go at this crossword.

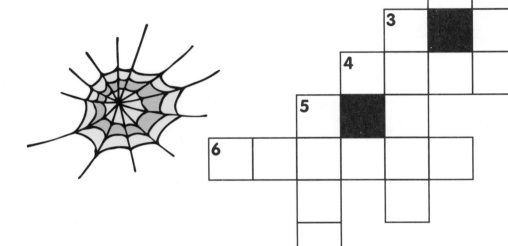

1. My kite flew…

2. Opposite of day

3. Don't turn left, turn…

4. Something you turn on to see

5. My tie is too…

6. The spider gave me a…

Prefix un

A prefix is a set of letters we put before a word (this word is known as the root word). Adding a prefix changes the meaning of a word. For example if you add **un**, **seen** becomes **unseen**. **Seen** is the **root word**. Add **un** to the words below.

_____happy

_____do

_____load

_____fair

_____lock

Now look at these words.
What were the root words before **un** was added?
Write them below.

undone   _____

unable   _____

unfit   _____

unkind   _____

unzip   _____

Balloon words

Fill the balloon with as many words as you can with the sound **oo** in them. 10 is good, 15 is brilliant and over 20 is out of this world! Here's one to start you off:

balloon

moon lagoon

Compound words

Compound words are two words joined together to make a new word. For example, farm + yard = farmyard.
Draw a line to connect the words that make up a compound word.

foot   pot

play   work

tea   ball

hand   brush

sea   room

home   chair

tooth   side

arm   bag

Contractions

We use something called an **apostrophe** to shorten words.

Here it is:

The apostrophe takes the place of the missing letter/letters. Look at the examples below and circle the letters that have been missed out.

e.g.   can not ➡ can't

should not ➡ shouldn't

was not ➡ wasn't

I would ➡ I'd

you are ➡ you're

you have ➡ you've

shall not ➡ shan't

did not ➡ didn't

I am ➡ I'm

Answers

CVC words
c<u>a</u>t, b<u>e</u>d, f<u>a</u>n, c<u>o</u>w, d<u>o</u>g, h<u>e</u>n, n<u>u</u>t

Which vowels are missing?
k<u>i</u>ng, fl<u>a</u>g, b<u>i</u>rd, fr<u>o</u>g, dr<u>u</u>m, sh<u>i</u>p, h<u>a</u>rp, m<u>a</u>st, sw<u>i</u>m

'ch', 'sh', 'th' and 'wh' words
ch- <u>ch</u>op, <u>ch</u>ip
sh- <u>sh</u>ell, wi<u>sh</u>, fi<u>sh</u>
th- mo<u>th</u>, <u>th</u>in, wi<u>th</u>
wh- <u>wh</u>en
<u>sh</u>ape, wa<u>sh</u>, <u>ch</u>ur<u>ch</u>, wi<u>sh</u> or wi<u>th</u>, mu<u>ch</u> or mu<u>sh</u>, whi<u>ch</u>

Ending in 'll', 'ss', 'ff', 'zz' and 'ck'
she<u>ll</u>, mo<u>ss</u> or mo<u>ck</u>, so<u>ck</u>, du<u>ll</u> or du<u>ff</u> or du<u>ck</u>, be<u>ll</u>, bu<u>ll</u> or bu<u>zz</u> or bu<u>ck</u> or bu<u>ff</u>, fi<u>ll</u> or fi<u>zz</u>

ss- mo<u>ss</u>, pa<u>ss</u>
ll- ba<u>ll</u>, sha<u>ll</u>,
zz- fi<u>zz</u>, bu<u>zz</u>
ck- blo<u>ck</u>, mu<u>ck</u>
ff- flu<u>ff</u>

Thinking of fishing
-ng thi<u>ng</u>, si<u>ng</u>, alo<u>ng</u>
-nk li<u>nk</u>, pla<u>nk</u>, spri<u>nk</u>le, clu<u>nk</u>
b. slick

Words ending in 'tch' and 've'
–tch stopwa<u>tch</u>, ha<u>tch</u>, wi<u>tch</u>, ca<u>tch</u>
–ve glo<u>ve</u>, hi<u>ve</u>, li<u>ve</u>

Words ending in 's' and 'es'
1 clap cats, thanks, spends, rocks, lamps, bags, balls, dogs
2 claps foxes, hatches, witches, catches, matches, boxes

Comparisons
fast, faster, fastest
tall, taller, tallest
low, lower, lowest
kind, kinder, kindest
grand, grander, grandest

Words ending in 'er' and 'est'
-er slower, quicker, hunter, lower, player, older, harder, flower, stronger, shower

-est slowest, quickest, lowest, oldest, hardest, strongest
both slow, quick, low, old, hard, strong

Words ending in 'ay' and 'oy'
may, stray, stay, lay, ray, tray, way, yay, boy, toy, joy, coy.
Did you find anymore?

c	l	s	p	x	v	g	t	f
s	a	t	y	p	m	e	f	t
t	y	r	a	v	a	t	x	o
a	l	a	w	k	y	r	m	y
y	z	y	z	w	f	a	a	g
s	t	b	y	h	k	y	f	s
u	y	c	o	y	s	b	h	j
h	z	a	b	j	o	y	n	e
t	e	b	d	h	w	t	n	v

You're the teacher!
correct rain, wait, train, afraid, fail, tail
incorrect oyl, spoyl, joyn, poynt, soyl, boyl

Five alive

x	n	y	l	i	k	e	m	x	x
h	i	j	g	r	d	k	j	s	t
p	n	b	l	i	s	a	h	e	i
a	e	m	i	d	i	c	i	o	m
l	y	f	n	e	d	w	d	h	e
i	l	i	e	s	t	r	e	t	h
f	i	v	d	s	i	d	e	u	e
e	k	e	a	m	r	s	w	d	k
l	i	n	m	h	i	k	e	b	i
x	q	m	y	x	y	b	o	i	k

Words with 'ar' and 'ee' st<u>ar</u>, g<u>ar</u>den, sh<u>ee</u>p, asl<u>ee</u>p, c<u>ar</u>, h<u>ar</u>p, p<u>ar</u>k, b<u>ee</u>

Words with 'ea'
dr<u>ea</u>m, <u>ea</u>ch, h<u>ea</u>t, n<u>ea</u>t, <u>ea</u>t, ch<u>ea</u>t, h<u>ea</u>d, h<u>ea</u>vy, st<u>ea</u>dy, inst<u>ea</u>d, d<u>ea</u>f

Words with 'er'
1. bitter, 2. summer, 3. under, 4. → winter, 4. ↓ warmer, 5. sister

Scramble mania!
bird, shirt, girl, third, nurse, chair, curls, burn, airplane

On the right road
b<u>oa</u>t, t<u>oa</u>st, g<u>oa</u>l, r<u>oa</u>d, c<u>oa</u>ch

Words with 'ew' and 'ue'
-ew grew, new, flew, crew
-ue glue, Tuesday, cue, tissue, true, blue

Words with 'ou' and 'ow'
c<u>ow</u>, sn<u>ow</u>, b<u>ow</u>, fl<u>ow</u>er, t<u>ow</u>n, cr<u>ow</u>n, h<u>ou</u>se, s<u>ou</u>nd, m<u>ou</u>se

Words ending in 'y'
lorr<u>y</u>, fl<u>y</u>, part<u>y</u>, bab<u>y</u>, famil<u>y</u>, sp<u>y</u>

Whales and dolphins
Correct spellings are: dolphin, elephant, alphabet, phone.
<u>wh</u>eel, <u>wh</u>ale, <u>wh</u>ip

ie or igh?
1. high, 2. night, 3. right, 4. light, 5. tight, 6. fright

Prefix -un
<u>un</u>happy, <u>un</u>do, <u>un</u>load, <u>un</u>fair, <u>un</u>lock
done, able, fit, kind, zip

Balloon words
food, mood, good, roof, proof, cool, tool, boom, gloom, spoon, soon, scoop, hoot, moor, poor.
Did you find anymore **oo** words?

Compound words
football, playroom, teapot, handbag, seaside, homework, toothbrush, armchair

Contractions
should n<u>o</u>t
was n<u>o</u>t
I w<u>o</u>uld
you <u>a</u>re
you h<u>a</u>ve
shall n<u>o</u>t
did n<u>o</u>t
I <u>a</u>m

Reading and Writing

In Year One (age 5+) your child is expected to be able to:

• Read common exception words, noting unusual correspondences between spelling and sound, and identify where these occur in the word.

• Read words of more than one syllable that contain taught GPCs.

• Write sentences by: saying aloud what they are going to write about; composing sentences orally before writing down; sequencing sentences to create short narratives; re-reading their work to check it makes sense.

• Discuss what they have written with others.

• Read their writing aloud clearly enough to be heard by their class.

Glossary

GPCs: This stands for grapheme-phoneme correspondence in phonics and is the relationship between sounds and the letters which represent those sounds. This is also referred to as 'letter-sound correspondences'.

Alphabet blocks

Finish writing the letters of the alphabet on these blocks.

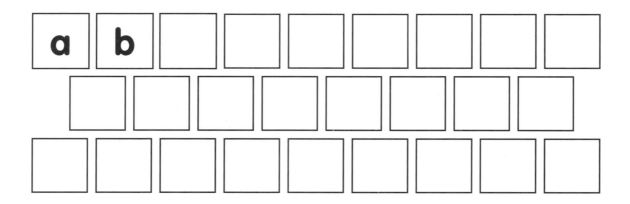

What letters do these objects begin with?
Draw lines to join each object to the correct letter block.

Ordering

Look at the words below. Put them in alphabetical order.

tent   mitten   witch   tree

lamp   clown   duck

_____

_____

_____

_____

_____

_____

_____

Find the vowels

Vowels are the name we give to the letters **a**, **e**, **i**, **o** and **u**.
Find them below and circle them. There should be **25** in total.

a   t   c   t

z   f   e   v

a

o   i   s

o   i

u

b   j   o

y   u

e   w

u   u

a   e

m   h

i   i

e   n

b   o

x   a

d   a   i   u

o   g

g   e

Find the consonants

Consonants are the name we give to letters that are not vowels.
Find them below and circle them. There should be **25** in total.

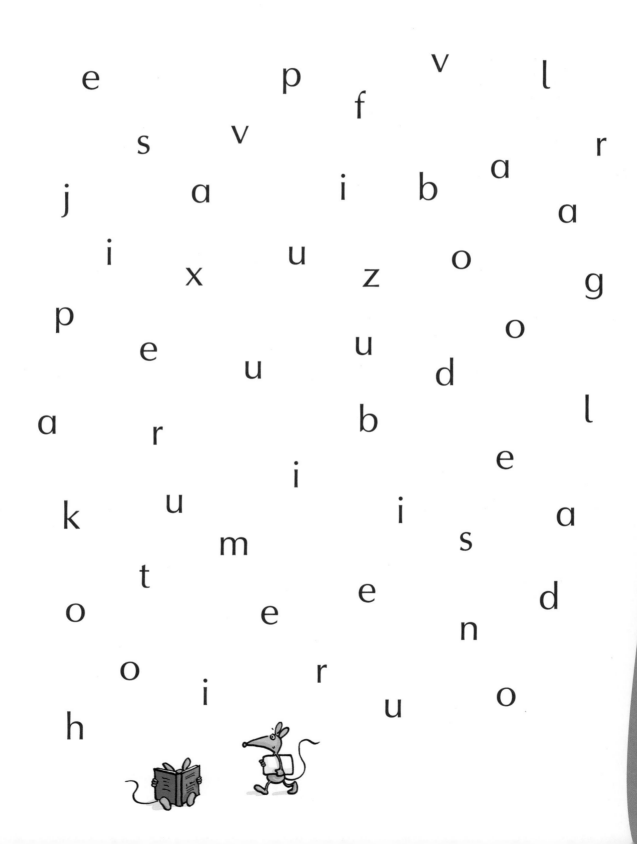

Missing vowels

Fill in the missing vowels to complete the words below.
Hint: The vowels are **a**, **e**, **i**, **o** and **u**.

c___t

b___d

j___r

f___n

d___g

m__g

h___n

n___t

b__x

k__ng

fl___g

st___p

fr___g

dr___m

sh__p

h___rp

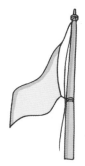

m___st

sw__m

Missing consonants

Write the correct consonant at the start of each word.
Hint: Consonants are letters that are not vowels.

__rog

__ree

__ocket

__able

__ar

__lock

__ock

__rab

__ rush

Reading rhyme

Complete the nursery rhyme using the words in the boxes.
Write in the missing words.

ten   finger   four   go   you

One, Two Three, Four, Five

One, two, three, _____ , five,

Once I caught a fish alive,

Six, seven, eight, nine, _____ ,

Then I let it _____ again.

Why did _____ let it go?

Because it bit my finger so.

Which _____ did it bite?

This little finger on the right.

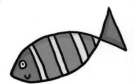

Reading and writing

Look at the pictures below. Under each is a sentence with a word missing. Choose the correct word from the boxes below and write it in.

books   **cat**   **balloons**   **tree**

The _____ is chasing the dog.

Erin likes sitting in the _____.

Joe and Samir have

_____.

Jason loves _____.

Reading and matching

Write the correct sentence beside the pictures.

The scared dog is being chased by a cat!
Jason is quietly reading his book.
The boys carefully hold on to their balloons.
Erin is hiding in the tall tree.

_____

_____

_____

_____

_____

_____

_____

That's a capital!

Words that are the names of people or places are given **capital letters**. These are called **proper nouns**. Look at the words below and circle the ones that should have capital letters.

computer

olivia

england

hippo

scotland

james

france

wales

apple

boat

bicycle

trees

book

carrot

fiona

Now look at the sentences below and circle the words that should have **capital letters**. Remember the first word of any sentence should also start with a capital letter.

a flag flutters in sean's hand.

julia would like to go to america.

surriya is going to pakistan to see her grandparents.

falling leaves and conkers remind chris of autumn.

the birds fly all the way to africa in winter.

Now write your own sentence using capital letters. Try to make sure it includes the name of a person and a place.

_____

_____

_____

Capitals and full stops

Remember we use **capital letters** to show proper nouns and the start of sentences. We finish sentences with a **full stop**. Rearrange these words to make sentences and write them on the lines below. Remember to use capital letters and full stops!

inside played james football the house

_____

australia live kangaroos in koala bears and

_____

cold is december in it wet and

_____

has brothers called susan two and jim niall

_____

It's your turn to be the teacher! Get a red pencil and put a circle around the letters that should have **capital letters** and write in the **full stops**.

1. "i like porridge," goldilocks muttered as she ran away

2. hippos and giraffes live in africa

3. if I lived in the north pole i might see father christmas

4. the capital city of england is london

5. james has 3 brothers; joseph, simon and peter, they live in bristol

6. the space rocket flew to jupiter

Are you asking or telling?

We use **question marks** to show that we are asking something.
Do you see that dot under the squiggle?
A question mark takes the place of a full stop.
Trace over the following question marks and finish the row.

? ? ?

Read the following sentences. Some are asking you something.
You need to put a question mark after these ones. The others are
statements. They tell you something and just need a full stop.

1. What is your favourite colour

2. I don't like ice cream

3. Birds fly through the air

4. Do you want to go to the park

5. Which cake would you like

6. Africa and Asia are both continents

Comma capers

We use **commas** for different reasons. One of the reasons is when we list things.

e.g. I went to the shop and I bought an apple**,** a banana and an orange. Don't forget to add **and** before the last item in the list.

Fill in the gaps with nouns (things).

I went to the shop and I bought a

_____, a _____

and a _____.

I went on holiday and I took a

_____, a _____

and a _____.

For my birthday I would like a

_____, a _____

and a _____.

Punctuation matters!

Read the passage. Write in the missing **commas** and circle any words that should have **capital letters**. Can you spot any questions that should be followed by a **question mark**? If so, put them in!

susan was amazed, she had reached into her bag and to her surprise pulled out an elephant, a baby chimpanzee and an orange. How did they all fit in there. I just don't know! but that wasn't all, there were more things in the magical bag. there was a book a tin of tuna half an apple and a hammer. susan hadn't put them in there so the question was, who had. who would put such things in a bag.

What would you expect to find in your school bag? Write a sentence below using capital letters and commas.

_____

_____

_____

Prepositions

Prepositions tell us where something is.
Is it **in front of**, **before**, **after**, **behind**, **under**, **over**, **on**, **in** or **on top of** something? Look at the picture. Write two sentences about the picture using one of the prepositions above in each.

_____

_____

_____

_____

Little Red Riding Hood

Read the story and answer the questions on the opposite page.

1.

Little Red Riding Hood decided to visit her sick grandmother.

2.

When she was picking some flowers in the forest, she met a wolf.

3.

When Little Red Riding Hood arrived at the house, the wolf had dressed up as her grandmother.

4.

"My what big teeth you have," said Little Red Riding Hood.
"All the better to eat you with!" cried the wolf.

5.

The wolf leapt out of bed and jumped on poor Little Red Riding Hood.

6.

Luckily, a woodcutter was passing by and rescued her from the wicked wolf.

1. Who was Little Red Riding Hood going to visit?

_____

2. Who did she meet in the forest?

_____

3. What was she doing when she met the wolf?

_____

4. Who did the wolf pretend to be?

_____

5. Who saved Little Red Riding Hood?

_____

What happens next?

Read the passage of text below. Write the next two sentences to continue the story. What do you think happens next?

Eli walked down the path, through the shaded trees. He could hear the birds singing. Eli wondered what the birds were saying. Then he heard a voice saying, "Hello Eli!"
Eli couldn't see anyone, so he walked on down the path towards the cottage when he heard a crunch on the path. He turned and there stood a bear. A small bear. Wearing a hat and a pair of sunglasses. It waved at him, smiled and stepped slowly towards Eli.

_____

_____

_____

_____

Awesome adjectives

Adjectives are words that help us understand more about nouns (things). Adjectives give us more detail.
e.g. the **small** dog, the **large** tree, the **green** apple.
Underline the adjectives in the following sentences.

The small boy ate the big apple.

A fluffy cat sat in the red basket.

The dark clouds made the afternoon gloomy and dull.

The orange crayon wished he could colour in a huge dinosaur.

Now write your own sentence using as many **adjectives** as you can.

_____

_____

_____

A day at the beach

Describe the picture below in two sentences. Make sure that you use **adjectives** to make them more interesting.

_____

_____

_____

_____

_____

Labels

In non-fiction, labels can be used on the pictures to help us understand the information. Write the correct labels in the boxes using the words below.

neck   leg   horn   ear

hoof   tail

Hello up there!

Read the passage below and answer the questions.

Giraffes are the tallest land animals. A giraffe could look into a second floor window without even having to stand on its tiptoes! A giraffe's 180 centimetre long neck weighs about 270 kilograms. The legs of a giraffe are also 180 centimetres long. The back legs look shorter than the front legs, but they are about the same length.

There is only one species of giraffe. They live in Africa. Some giraffes, from Kenya, have spots that look like oak leaves. Other kinds have a square-shaped pattern that looks like the giraffe is covered by a net. Some scientists think that the giraffe's pattern is for camouflage.

Both male and female giraffes have two distinct hair-covered horns called ossicones. Male giraffes use their horns to fight with one another. They are quite shy animals. Giraffes have blue coloured tongues. This is because they eat a lot of leaves. They use their tongues to rip the leaves off the trees so their tongues spend a long time in the sun. Because they are a blue colour, they don't get sunburnt!

1. What are the tallest land animals?

_____

2. How long is a giraffe's neck?

_____

3. Where do giraffes live?

_____

4. What type of leaves do the spots sometimes look like?

_____

5. How many horns does a giraffe have?

_____

6. What colour is a giraffe's tongue?

_____

7. How does this help giraffes?

_____

Read this poster about a circus that is coming to town.

★ ★ ★ ★ ★

The Big Top Circus
presents...

Fred the fearless fire-eater,
Justin the juggler,
Clive the crazy clown,
Tracey the trapeze artist,
Alan the acrobat
... and lots, lots more.

So join us at the Big Top for a
fun-filled evening to remember!

Date: Saturday 3rd July
Time: 7pm **Place:** Woodside Park
Price: adults £2.50   children £1.75

Using the information from the poster, answer the questions below by putting a tick in the correct box.

1. What is the name of the circus?

☐ Small Top   ☐ Big Top

☐ Big Hat

2. What is Alan's job?

☐ an acrobat   ☐ a clown

☐ a juggler

3. Who is the trapeze artist?

☐ Tracey   ☐ Tara

☐ Alan

4. What time does the show start?

☐ 6pm   ☐ 7am

☐ 7pm

5. How much are tickets for children?

☐ £1.75   ☐ £2.20

☐ £17.50

More questions!

Read the poster on page 124 again.
Now answer these questions.

1. Where is the circus being held?

_____

2. Why is Fred described as fearless?

_____

3. What else might you see at the circus?

_____

4. Would you rather be a clown, a juggler,
a fire-eater or a trapeze artist?

_____

5. Why?

_____

_____

_____

Improving writing

Can you make these sentences more interesting?

e.g. The worm was in the earth ➤
The long, thin wriggly worm squirmed into the warm earth.

The leaves fell from the tree.

_____

_____

James bought a cake.

_____

_____

Answers

Alphabet blocks
chair, **t**oilet, **r**ose or **f**lower, **f**ork, **s**tamp, **d**rum

Ordering
clown, **d**uck, **l**amp, **m**itten, **t**ent, **t**ree, **w**itch

Missing vowels
c**a**t, b**e**d, j**a**r, f**a**n, d**o**g, m**u**g, h**e**n, n**u**t, b**o**x, k**i**ng, fl**a**g, st**o**p, fr**o**g, dr**u**m, sh**i**p, h**a**rp, m**a**st, sw**i**m

Missing consonants
frog, **tr**ee, **r**ocket, **t**able, **c**ar, **cl**ock, **s**ock, **cr**ab, **br**ush

Reading rhyme
One, two, three, <u>four</u>, five,
Once I caught a fish alive,
Six, seven, eight, nine, <u>ten</u>,
Then I let it <u>go</u> again.
Why did <u>you</u> let it go?
Because it bit my finger so.
Which <u>finger</u> did it bite?
This little finger on the right.

Reading and writing
The <u>cat</u> is chasing the dog.
Erin likes sitting in the <u>tree</u>.
Joe and Samir have <u>balloons</u>.
Jason loves <u>books</u>.

That's a capital!
<u>O</u>livia, <u>E</u>ngland, <u>S</u>cotland, <u>J</u>ames, <u>F</u>rance, <u>W</u>ales, <u>F</u>iona

<u>A</u> flag flutters in <u>S</u>ean's hand.
<u>J</u>ulia would like to go to <u>A</u>merica.
<u>S</u>urriya is going to <u>P</u>akistan to see her grandparents.
<u>F</u>alling leaves and conkers remind <u>C</u>hris of autumn.
<u>T</u>he birds fly all the way to <u>A</u>frica in winter.

Capitals and full stops
<u>J</u>ames played football inside the house<u>.</u>
<u>K</u>oala bears and kangaroos live in <u>A</u>ustralia<u>.</u>
<u>I</u>t is cold and wet in <u>D</u>ecember<u>.</u>
<u>S</u>usan has two brothers called <u>J</u>im and <u>N</u>iall<u>.</u>

1. "<u>I</u> like porridge," Goldilocks muttered as she ran away<u>.</u>
2. <u>H</u>ippos and giraffes live in <u>A</u>frica<u>.</u>
3. <u>I</u>f I lived in the <u>N</u>orth <u>P</u>ole <u>I</u> might see <u>F</u>ather <u>C</u>hristmas<u>.</u>
4. <u>T</u>he capital city of <u>E</u>ngland is <u>L</u>ondon<u>.</u>
5. <u>J</u>ames has 3 brothers; <u>J</u>oseph, <u>S</u>imon and <u>P</u>eter, they live in <u>B</u>ristol<u>.</u>
6. <u>T</u>he space rocket flew to <u>J</u>upiter<u>.</u>

Are you asking or telling?
1. What is your favourite colour<u>?</u>
2. I don't like ice cream<u>.</u>
3. Birds fly through the air<u>.</u>
4. Do you want to go to the park<u>?</u>
5. Which cake would you like<u>?</u>
6. Africa and Asia are both continents<u>.</u>

Punctuation matters!
<u>S</u>usan was amazed, she had reached into her bag and<u>,</u> to her surprise<u>,</u> pulled out an elephant, a baby chimpanzee and an orange. How did they all fit in there<u>?</u> I just don't know! <u>B</u>ut that wasn't all, there were more things in the magical bag. <u>T</u>here was a book<u>,</u> a tin of tuna<u>,</u> half an apple and a hammer. <u>S</u>usan hadn't put them in there<u>,</u> so the question was, who had<u>?</u> <u>W</u>ho would put such things in a bag<u>?</u>

Little Red Riding Hood
1. Her sick grandmother.
2. She met a wolf.
3. She was picking some flowers.
4. Her grandmother.
5. A woodcutter.

Awesome adjectives
The <u>small</u> boy ate the <u>big</u> apple.
A <u>fluffy</u> cat sat in the <u>red</u> basket.
The <u>dark</u> clouds made the afternoon <u>gloomy</u> and <u>dull</u>.
The <u>orange</u> crayon wished he could colour in a <u>huge</u> dinosaur.

Labels

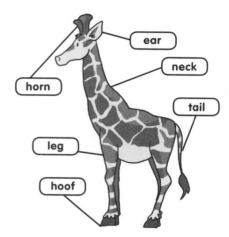

Hello up there!
1. Giraffes.
2. 180 centimetres.
3. Africa.
4. Oak leaves.
5. Two.
6. Blue.
7. They don't get sunburnt.

Roll up!
1. Big Top.
2. an acrobat.
3. Tracey.
4. 7pm.
5. £1.75.

More questions!
1. Woodside Park.
2. He eats fire.
3. Tightrope walker, ring master, strong man, lion tamer.